Karen

MOTHER GOOSE

Rhymes with Music

Illustrations by

ESMÉ EVE

Music arranged by

ALFRED WOULDS

Mother Goose

RHYMES WITH MUSIC

GROSSET & DUNLAP
Publishers • New York

Contents

Index of First Lines

OLD MOTHER GOOSE,
When she wanted to wander,
Would ride through the air
On a very fine gander.

OLD MOTHER GOOSE

Music by
ALEC ROWLEY

By permission of J. Curwen & Sons Ltd., from "Little Robin and other small songs."

SEE-SAW, MARGERY DAW

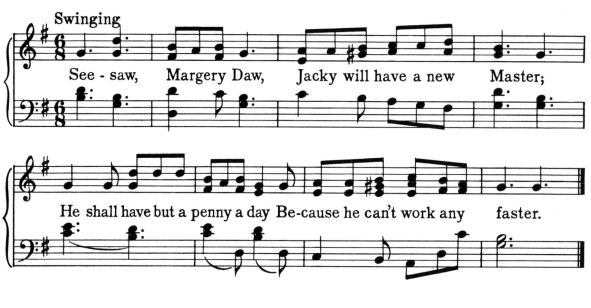

See - saw, Margery Daw, Jacky will have a new Master;

He shall have but a penny a day Be-cause he can't work any faster.

LAVENDER'S BLUE

Lavender's blue, diddle, diddle, Lavender's green;

When I am King, diddle, diddle, You shall be Queen.

SING A SONG

Happily

Sing a song of sixpence, A pocket full of rye;
The king was in his counting-house, Counting out his money

When the pie was opened The birds began to sing;
maid was in the garden, Hanging out the clothes

14

OF SIXPENCE

Four-and-twenty blackbirds Baked in a pie.
The queen was in the parlour Eating bread and honey; The

Was not that a dainty dish To set before a king?
Down came a blackbird And pecked off her nose.

PUSSY CAT, PUSSY CAT

Questioning

Pussy cat, pussy cat, where have you been? I've been up to London to look at the Queen. Pussy cat, pussy cat, what did you there? I frightened a little mouse under her chair.

JACK AND JILL

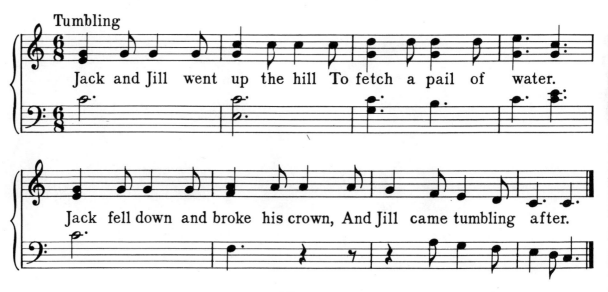

Tumbling

Jack and Jill went up the hill To fetch a pail of water.

Jack fell down and broke his crown, And Jill came tumbling after.

Pussy cat, pussy cat, where have you been?

Patting

Pat a-cake, pat-a-cake, baker's man! Bake me a cake as fast as you can.

Pat it, and prick it, and mark it with *B; And put it in the oven for *Baby and me.

*B is for Baby, or another name here.

HEY DIDDLE DIDDLE

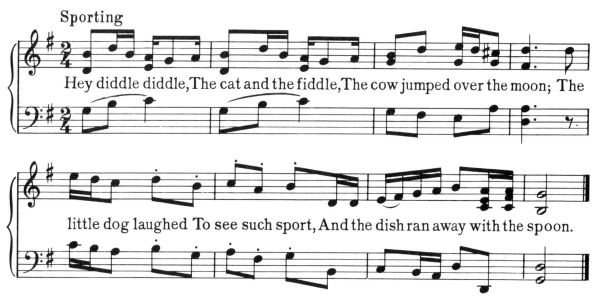

Sporting

Hey diddle diddle, The cat and the fiddle, The cow jumped over the moon; The

little dog laughed To see such sport, And the dish ran away with the spoon.

TOM, TOM, THE PIPER'S SON

Deliberately

Tom, Tom, the piper's son, Stole a pig and a - way did run. The
pig was eat and Tom was beat, And Tom went howling down the street.

LITTLE BO-PEEP

Simply

Little Bo-peep has lost her sheep, And doesn't know where to find them; Leave them alone, and they will come home, And bring their tails be-hind them.

MARY, MARY, QUITE CONTRARY

Prettily

Mary, Mary, quite contrary, How does your garden grow? With silver bells, and cockle shells, And pretty maids all in a row.

RIDE A COCK-HORSE TO BANBURY CROSS,
To see a fine lady upon a white horse.

RIDE A COCK-HORSE

As if riding

Ride a cock-horse to Banbury Cross, To see a fine lady up-on a white horse.

Rings on her fingers, and bells on her toes, She shall have music wher-ever she goes.

I LOVE LITTLE PUSSY

Lovingly

I love little pussy, her coat is so warm, And

if I don't hurt her she'll do me no harm.

BAA, BAA, BLACK SHEEP

Simply

Baa, baa, black sheep, Have you any wool? Yes, sir, yes, sir, Three bags full;

One for my master, One for my dame, And

one for the little boy Who lives down the lane.

LITTLE POLLY FLINDERS

Little Polly Flinders Sat among the cinders, Warming her pretty little toes; Her mother came and caught her, And whipped her little daughter For spoiling her nice new clothes.

27

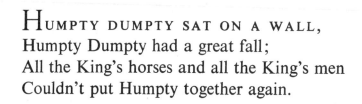

HUMPTY DUMPTY SAT ON A WALL,
Humpty Dumpty had a great fall;
All the King's horses and all the King's men
Couldn't put Humpty together again.

HUMPTY DUMPTY

Falling

Humpty Dumpty   sat on a wall,   Humpty Dumpty   had a great fall;

All the King's horses and all the King's men Couldn't put Humpty to-gether again.

GEORGIE PORGIE,
PUDDING AND PIE

Cowardly

Georgie Porgie,   pudding and pie,   Kissed the girls and made them cry.

When the boys came out to play,   Georgie Porgie   ran a-way.

29

DING, DONG, BELL,
Pussy's in the well!
Who put her in?
Little Tommy Thin.
Who pulled her out?
Little Tommy Stout.

30

DING, DONG, BELL

Pealing

Ding, dong, bell, Pussy's in the well! Who put her in?

Little Tommy Thin. Who pulled her out? Little Tommy Stout. What a

naughty boy was that, To drown poor pussy cat, Who never did him harm, But

killed all the mice in his father's barn!

SIMPLE SIMON MET A PIEMAN
  Going to the fair;
Says Simple Simon to the pieman,
  " Let me taste your ware."

Says the pieman to Simple Simon,
  " Show me first your penny."
Says Simple Simon to the pieman,
  " Indeed I have not any."

SIMPLE SIMON

Simple Simon met a pieman Going to the fair; Says

Simple Simon to the pieman, "Let me taste your ware."

TWINKLE, TWINKLE, LITTLE STAR

Twinkle, twinkle, little star, How I wonder what you are!

Up above the world so high, Like a diamond in the sky.

Twinkle, twinkle, little star, How I wonder what you are!

THREE BLIND MICE, SEE HOW THEY RUN!
They all ran after the farmer's wife,
Who cut off their tails with a carving knife,
Did ever you see such a thing in your life,
    As three blind mice?

THREE BLIND MICE

Three blind mice, see how they run! They all ran after the farmer's wife, Who cut off their tails with a carving knife, Did ever you see such a sight in your life, As three blind mice?

IF ALL THE WORLD WAS APPLE-PIE

Rhythmically

If all the world was apple-pie And all the sea was ink, And all the trees were bread and cheese, What should we have to drink?

HOT CROSS BUNS!

As a street crier would

Hot cross buns! Hot cross buns! One a penny, two a penny, Hot cross buns!

If you have no daughters give them to your sons.

One a penny, two a penny, Hot cross buns!

HOT CROSS BUNS!
Hot cross buns!
One a penny,
Two a penny,
Hot cross buns!

THE QUEEN OF HEARTS
She made some tarts,
All on a summer's day;
The Knave of Hearts,
He stole those tarts,
And took them clean away.

The King of Hearts
Called for the tarts,
And beat the Knave full sore.
The Knave of Hearts
Brought back those tarts,
And vowed he'd steal no more.

THE QUEEN OF HEARTS

The Queen of Hearts She made some tarts, All
The King of Hearts Called for the tarts, And

on a summer's day; The Knave of Hearts, He
beat the Knave full sore. The Knave of Hearts Brought

stole those tarts, And took them clean a - way.
back those tarts, And vowed he'd steal no more.

HARK! HARK! THE DOGS DO BARK

Hark! hark! the dogs do bark, The beggars are coming to town,

Some in jags, some in rags, And one in a velvet gown.

LUCY LOCKET

Rhythmically

Lucy Locket lost her pocket,

Kitty Fisher found it; But ne'er a penny was there in it Ex-

cept the ribbon round it.

Lucy Locket is sung to the same tune as the next well-known song in this book, *Yankee Doodle*.

YANKEE DOODLE

Proudly

Yankee Doodle came to town, Riding on a pony; He stuck a feather in his cap, And called it maca - ron - i.

LITTLE MISS MUFFET
Sat on a tuffet,
Eating her curds and whey;
There came a big spider,
And sat down beside her,
And frightened Miss Muffet away.

LITTLE MISS MUFFET (P.56)

Frightened

Little Miss Muffet Sat on a tuffet, Eating her curds and whey; There came a big spider, And sat down beside her, And frightened Miss Muffet a-way.

HICKORY, DICKORY, DOCK

Tick tocking

Hickory, dickory, dock! The mouse ran up the clock. The

tick! tock! tick! tock! tick! tock! tick! tock!

clock struck one, The mouse ran down, Hickory, dickory, dock!

MARY HAD A LITTLE LAMB

Playfully

Mary had a little lamb, Its fleece was white as snow; And

ev'rywhere that Mary went The lamb was sure to go. It

followed her to school one day; That was against the rule; It

made the children laugh and play To see a lamb at school.

44

POLLY, PUT THE KETTLE ON

Playfully

Polly, put the kettle on, Polly, put the kettle on, Polly, put the

kettle on, And we'll all have tea. Sukey, take it off again, Sukey, take it

off again, Sukey, take it off again, And they've all gone a - way.

OLD KING COLE
Was a merry old soul,
And a merry old soul was he!
    He called for his pipe,
    And he called for his bowl,
And he called for his fiddlers three.

OLD KING COLE

Merrily

Old King Cole Was a merry old soul, And a merry old soul was he! He called for his pipe, And he called for his bowl, And he called for his fiddlers three. Every fiddler he had a fine fiddle, And a very fine fiddle had he, Then twee, tweedle dee went the fiddlers three, And so merry we will be.

I SAW THREE SHIPS COME SAILING BY

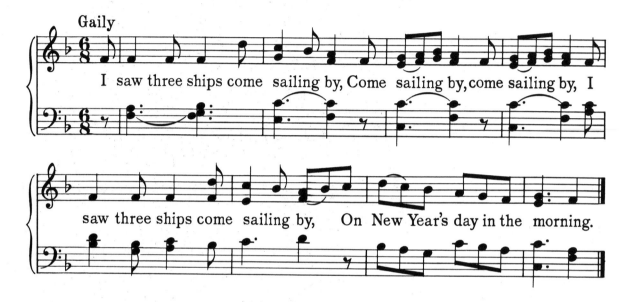

Gaily

I saw three ships come sailing by, Come sailing by, come sailing by, I
saw three ships come sailing by, On New Year's day in the morning.

And what do you think was in them then,
 Was in them then, was in them then?
And what do you think was in them then,
 On New Year's day in the morning?

Three pretty girls were in them then,
 Were in them then, were in them then,
Three pretty girls were in them then,
 On New Year's day in the morning.

One could whistle, and one could sing,
 And one could play on the violin;
Such joy there was at my wedding,
 On New Year's day in the morning.

48

DANCE TO YOUR DADDIE

Dancing

Dance to your daddie, My bonnie laddie; Dance to your daddie, my bonnie lamb!

You shall get a fishie, On a little dishie: You shall get a fishie, when the boat comes hame.

Dance to your daddie, My bonnie laddie; Dance to your daddie, my bonnie lamb!

OH WHERE IS MY LITTLE DOG GONE?

Worried

Oh where, oh where is my little dog gone? Oh where, oh where can he be?

With his ears cut short and his tail cut long, Oh where, oh where is he?

49

I HAD A LITTLE NUT TREE,
  Nothing would it bear
But a silver nutmeg
  And a golden pear.
The King of Spain's daughter
  Came to visit me,
And all for the sake
  Of my little nut tree.

50

I HAD A LITTLE NUT TREE

Fairly slowly

I had a little nut tree, Nothing would it bear

But a silver nutmeg And a golden pear. The King of Spain's daughter

Came to visit me, And all for the sake Of my little nut tree.

RING-A-RING O' ROSES

Ring - a - ring o' roses A pocketful of

posies, Atishoo! Atishoo! We all fall down.

51

THERE WAS A JOLLY MILLER ONCE

Jolly

There was a jolly miller once Lived on the river Dee; He worked and sang from morn till night, No lark more blithe than

he. And this the burden of his song For ever used to

be, I care for nobody, no! not I, Since nobody cares for me.

THIS OLD MAN

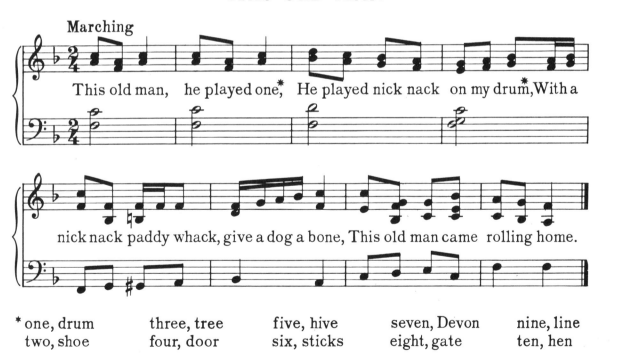

Marching

This old man, he played one,* He played nick nack on my drum, With a

nick nack paddy whack, give a dog a bone, This old man came rolling home.

*one, drum	three, tree	five, hive	seven, Devon	nine, line
two, shoe	four, door	six, sticks	eight, gate	ten, hen

By permission of J. Curwen & Sons Ltd. and B. Feldman & Co. Ltd.

RUB-A-DUB-DUB,
Three men in a tub,

RUB-A-DUB-DUB

Knavishly

Rub-a-dub-dub, Three men in a tub, And who d'you think they be? The

butcher, the baker, The candlestick-maker, So turn out the knaves all three.

TWO LITTLE   DICKY-BIRDS

Two little dicky-birds Sitting on a wall, One named Peter, The other named Paul.

Fly away, Peter!   Fly away, Paul!   Come back, Peter!   Come back, Paul!

LITTLE JACK HORNER

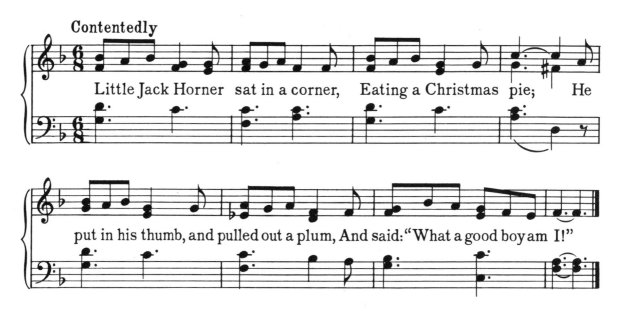

Little Jack Horner sat in a corner,   Eating a Christmas pie;   He

put in his thumb, and pulled out a plum, And said:"What a good boy am I!"

JINGLE BELLS

Jingling

Jingle bells, jingle bells, jingle all the way,   Oh what fun it is to run In a

one-horse open sleigh!   Jingle bells, jingle bells, jingle all the way,

Oh what fun it is   to run In a   one - horse open sleigh!

The TWELFTH day of Christmas,
My true love sent to me
Twelve lords a-leaping,
Eleven ladies dancing,
Ten pipers piping,
Nine drummers drumming,
Eight maids a-milking,
Seven swans a-swimming,
Six geese a-laying,
Five gold rings,
Four colly birds,
Three French hens,
Two turtle-doves, and
A partridge in a pear-tree.

the first day of Christmas

THE TWELVE DAYS OF CHRISTMAS

59

"COME, LET'S TO BED"

Drowsily

"Come, let's to bed," says Sleepy-head; "Tarry a while," says Slow; "Put on the pan," Says Greedy Nan, "Let's sup before we go."

MATTHEW, MARK, LUKE AND JOHN

Prayerfully

Matthew, Mark and Luke and John, Bless the bed that I lie on.

Four angels to my bed, Two to bottom, two to head,

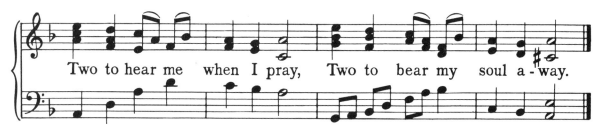

Two to hear me when I pray, Two to bear my soul a-way.

From English Folk Songs for Schools by permission of J.Curwen & Sons Ltd.